Delights for ladies to adorn their persons, tables and closets. Baths, essences, pot-pourri, powders, perfumes, sweet-scented waters.

RECIPES
for
ROSES

Copper Beech Publishing

Published in Great Britain by
Copper Beech Publishing Ltd
© Jan Barnes Copper Beech Publishing Ltd 2001

Compiled by Jan Barnes
Editor Julie Lessels

ISBN 1 898617-31-7

A CIP catalogue record for this book is available from the
British Library.

Copper Beech Publishing Ltd
P O Box 159 East Grinstead
Sussex England RH19 4FS

Including

How to dry rose leaves
Pot pourri
A sweet jar
A sweet powder for bags
A red rose love charm
Perfumed silk bags
Bags to lay with linen
Perfumed bags to remove
musty smells
Syrup of roses
To procure sleep
To cure the head-ache
A curious perfume
To make the teeth
beautifully white
Ladies' water
Musk rose water
To preserve the natural
colours of the flowers
A common useful
perfumed powder
Spirit of roses
Scarlet lip salve
Fragrant pastils to burn
A powder to cause sleep
A powder to last
seven years

Washballs
A scented jar
A pomander
To preserve a single
flower
Rose beads for a rosary
Perfume for the house
Perfume for chambers
Perfumes to burn
Rose pastils
Extracting essential oils
A sweet water
A water for the head and
the memory
A water to perfume
clothes
A sweet water using a
thousand roses
To perfume gloves
A rare and pleasant
damask water
A sweet water
Scenting snuff
The rose leaf cushion
Midsummer 1896

HOW TO DRY ROSE LEAVES IN A MOST EXCELLENT MANNER

Put in your roses in a sieve, first clipping away the whites that they may be all of one colour, lay them about one inch in thickness in the sieve. Let them yet remain without stirring, till the uppermost of them be fully dried, then stir them together. Leave about one other half hour; and if you find them dry in the top, stir them together again, and continue this until they are thoroughly dried; then put them hot into an earthen pot having a narrow mouth. Stop it with cork and wet parchment and hang your pot in a chimney, or near a continual fire, and so they will keep exceeding fair in colour and most delicate in scent. And if you fear their relenting, take the rose leaves about Candlemas, and put them once again into a sieve, stirring them up and down often till they be dry: and then put them again hot into your pots.

ANOTHER WAY FOR THE DRYING OF ROSE LEAVES

Dry the roses in the heat of a hot sunny day, turning them up and down till they be dry then put them up into glasses well stopped and air-tight, keeping your glasses in warm places; and thus you may keep all flowers; but herbs, after they are dried in this manner, are best kept in paper bags.

ROSES AND GILLYFLOWERS

Cover a rose that is fresh and in the bud, and gathered in a fair day after the dew is ascended, with the whites of eggs well beaten, and presently strew thereon the fine powder of sugar. Put them up in air-tight pots, setting the pots in a cool place in sand or gravel: with a fillip at any time you may shake this enclosure.

TO DRY OR KEEP ROSES

Take the buds of damask roses before they are fully blown, pull the leaves and lay them on boards, in a room where the heat of the sun may not come at them. As they are drying, let a large still be made warm, and lay them on the top of it till they are crisp; but they must not lie so long as to change their colour. Spread them thin; and when thoroughly dried, press them down into a earthen pan, and keep close covered.

DRY POT-POURRI

Gather the following flowers and herbs on a fine day: roses, thyme, rosemary, sweet marjoram, lavender, myrtle, southernwood, balm, sweet basil, bay leaves. Dry them thoroughly by spreading on sieves in the shade. When dry, rub all to powder and add at discretion pounded cloves, musk and orris root.

ANOTHER RECIPE FOR POT-POURRI

*D*ried pale and red rose petals, one handful of lavender flowers, acacia flowers, clove gillyflowers, orange-flower petals, one wineglassful of mignonette flowers, one teaspoonful of heliotrope flowers, or two of musk, thirty drops of oil of vetiver, five drops oil of sandalwood, ten drops oil of myrtle, twenty drops oil of jonquil. Dry the petals and flowers, add the other ingredients and put into a hermetically sealed jar for some time.

A SWEET JAR

*F*our handfuls of damask roses, four handfuls of lavender flowers, two handfuls of orange flowers, two handfuls of cloves, carnations, also the flowers of sweet marjoram, thyme, rosemary, myrtle and mint, of each one handful. One seville orange stuck with cloves well dried and pounded and one ounce of cinnamon, the rind of two lemons and six bay leaves.

All the ingredients must be thoroughly dried but not in the sun. Mix them all together in a jar with salt.

It is best to gather the flowers in the forenoon, before the heat of the day has faded the petals in any way.

A DRY POT-POURRI

$\mathcal{T}$o a basin of dried scented roses add a handful of dried knotted marjoram, lemon thyme, rosemary, lavender flowers all well dried, the rind of one lemon and one orange dried to powder, six dried bay leaves, half an ounce of bruised cloves, a teaspoon of allspice, half an ounce of cinnamon and a good pinch of sandalwood.

Gather and dry the flowers and leaves all through the season, adding any others according to one's fancy but keeping the proportion of a basin of rose petals to a large handful of all the other ingredients put together. Store in a jar with a lid but the jar need not be air tight. Mix well together and stir occasionally.

TO MAKE SWEET POWDER FOR BAGS

Take of rose leaves dried two handfuls, of orris four ounces, of dried marjoram one handful, cloves one ounce, benjamin two ounces, of white sanders and yellow of each one ounce; beat all these into a gross powder, then put to it of musk a dram, of civet half a dram, and of ambergris half a dram, then put them into a taffety bag and use it.

The Red Rose Love Charm

'Pluck a full-blown red rose during the month
of June ... place in a white envelope and seal
with wax. Make an impression on the wax with
the third finger of your left hand. Now, place
the envelope under your pillow and carefully
note your dreams that night.

If you dream of water or silver, you will be
married within a year. A dream of animals,
birds or a looking glass means you will wait
five years for your wedding.'

PERFUMED SILK BAGS

Dry one pound of rose leaves in the shade, or at about four feet from a stove; cloves, caraway seeds, and allspice, of each one ounce; pound in a mortar, or grind in a mill; dried salt, a quarter of a pound. Mix all together, and put the compound into little silk bags.

BAGS TO SCENT LINEN

Take rose leaves dried in the shade, cloves beat to a powder and mace scraped; mix them together and put the composition into little muslin bags.

SWEET SCENTED BAGS TO LAY
WITH LINEN

Eight ounces of damask rose leaves, eight ounces of coriander seeds, eight ounces of sweet orris root, eight ounces of calamus aromaticus, one ounce of mace, one ounce of cinnamon, half an ounce of cloves, four drams of musk-powder, two drams of white loaf sugar, three ounces of lavender flowers and some of Rhodium wood. Beat them well together and make them in small silk bags.

Linen Cupboard.

Sweet bags placed in a lady's writing case
will add fragrance to the notepaper and
envelopes - a delicate reminder
of a summer garden full
of roses.

PERFUMED BAGS FOR REMOVING
MUSTY SMELLS FROM DRAWERS

Two ounces of dried rose petals, two ounces dried lavender flowers, two ounces yellow sanders, two ounces coriander seeds, two ounces orris root, two ounces calamus aromaticus, two ounces cloves, two ounces cinnamon bark, and one pound oak shavings. Reduce all to a coarse powder and fill linen bags with the mixture. These bags remove any musty smell from old furniture.

SYRUP OF ROSES

A singular manner of making the syrup of roses. Fill a basin three-quarters full of rainwater or rose water; put therein a convenient proportion of rose leaves.

Cover the basin and set it upon a pot of hot water (as you would usually bake a custard), in three quarters of an hour or one whole hour at most and you shall purchase the full strength and tincture of the rose. Then take out the leaves, wringing out all their liquor gently and steep more fresh leaves in the same water.

Continue this seven times and then make it up in a syrup and this syrup worketh more kindly than that which is made merely of the juice of the rose.

You may make sundry other syrups in this manner.

TO PROCURE SLEEP

Chop camomile and crumbs of brown bread. Boil with white wine vinegar and rose leaves. Let it heat till thick. Bind some round the temples and some to the soles of the feet.

A RECIPE FOR THE HEAD-ACHE

This is a most excellent recipe for the head-ache. Take red rose leaves, dried; mix wheat flour, vinegar and some houfleek. Boil them till thick. Spread, add this salve to a linen cloth and lay on forehead and temples.

Grief and pains of the head: because lettuces are owned by the moon, they cool and moisten what heat and dryness Mars causeth - the juice of lettuce, mixed or boiled with oil of roses and applied to the forehead and temples, procureth sleep and easeth the headache - Culpeper

A CURIOUS PERFUME

*B*oil, in two quarts of rose water, one ounce of storax and two ounces of gum benjamin, to which add, tied up in a piece of gauze or thin muslin, six cloves, bruised; half dram calamus aromaticus and a little lemon peel.

Cover the vessel up close and keep the ingredients boiling a great while. Drain off the liquor without strong pressure and let it stand till it deposit the sediment.

Keep for use in a box.

*Blossoms which are fairly strong scented
are the best.*

TO MAKE THE TEETH
BEAUTIFULLY WHITE

Take rose water, syrup of violets, clarified honey and plantain water, of each half an ounce, spirit of vitriol one ounce, mix them together. Rub the teeth with a linen rag moistened in this liquor and them rinse the mouth with equal parts of rose and plantain water.

LADIES' WATER

Take two handfuls and a half of red roses, rosemary flowers, lavender and spikenard, of each a handful; thyme, camomile flowers, sage of virtue, pennyroyal and marjoram, of each a handful, infuse in white wine four and twenty hours, then put the whole into an alembic. Sprinkle with a good white wine and throw on it a powder, one ounce and a half of cloves, gum benjamin, and storax. Strain and keep the distilled water in a bottle, well stopped.

MUSK ROSE WATER

*T*o make an excellent water, let the flowers of your roses be gathered two or three hours after sun rising in very fine weather. Take two handfuls of your musk rose leaves, put them into about a quart of fair water and a quarter of a pound of sugar, let this stand and steep for about half an hour, then take your water and flowers and pour them out of one vessel into another till such time as the water hath taken the scent and taste of the flowers, then set it in a cool place to cool and you will find it a most excellent scent-water.

TO PRESERVE THE NATURAL COLOURS OF FLOWERS

Take fine white sand, wash it till it contains no earth or salt, then dry it for use. When quite dry, fill a glass half full with the sand in the sun (or if in winter time in a room where a constant fire is kept). Stick in the flowers in their natural situation and cover gently with more sand just above the flower. Roses of a delicate colour recover their natural lustre by being exposed to a moderate vapour of brimstone.

A COMMON USEFUL PERFUMED POWDER

Take one pound dried rose leaves, same of florentine orris, gum benjamin two ounces storax one ounce, yellow sanders one ounce and a half cloves two drams and a little lemon peel. Reduce to a fine powder and mix with twenty pounds of starch. Mix well and then sift through a lawn sieve.

SPIRIT OF ROSES

*T*o make spirit of roses to burn, take twenty pounds of damask roses and beat them to a paste in a marble mortar. Put the paste, layer by layer with sea salt into a large stone jar. Sprinkle every layer of the paste about half an inch thick with salt and press the layers of roses as close together as possible. Cork the jar with a waxed cork, cover the top of the cork and the edges of the mouth of the jar with wax and place it six weeks in a cool place. After this time the jar will exhale a strong smell. Take five to six pounds of this fermented rose paste and put it into a common cucurbit and distill it with a very gentle fire in a vapour bath. After the last distillation you will have obtained a very fine scented water but not very spiritous.

The scent of spirit of roses is extremely sweet; if only two drops are mixed with a glass of water they impart to the water so high a perfume that it exceeds the best rose water.

A SCARLET LIP SALVE

Take hog's lard washed in rose water, half a pound red roses and a quarter of a pound damask roses bruised; knead them together and let them lie in that state two days. Then melt the hogs lard and strain it from the roses. Add a fresh quantity of the latter; knead them in the hog's lard and let them lie together two days as before; then gently simmer the mixture in a vapour bath. Press out the lard, and keep it for use in the same manner as other lip salves.

FRAGRANT PASTILS TO BURN

Pulverise a pound of the marc or residuum left in the still after making angelica water, likewise a large handful of roses and, with a sufficient quantity of gum tragacanth dissolved in rose water, beat them into a stiff paste which is to be rolled out upon a marble with a rolling pin and cut into lozenges or formed into pastils.

If you have a mind to ornament these pastils, cover them with leaf gold or silver.

A BAG TO CAUSE ONE TO SLEEP

Take dry rose leaves, keep them close in a glass to keep them sweet, then take powder of mints, and powder of cloves. Put the same to the rose leaves, then put all together in a bag, and take that to bed with you. It will cause you to sleep, and is good to smell unto at other times.

A POWDER TO LAST SEVEN YEARS

Take two ounces each of red and damask rose leaves, of purest orris one pound, of cloves three drams, coriander seed one dram, cyprus and calamus, of each half an ounce. Beat all together. Then take benzoin and storax of each three drams and powder them by themselves, then of musk and civet, each twenty grains. Mix these with the powder using a warm pestle, so little by little you may mix it with all the rest. You may put it up into your sweet bags and so keep them seven years.

WASHBALLS

To make a fine scented washball, take of the best white soap, half a pound, and shave it in thin slices with a knife then take two ounces and a half of florentine orris, three quarters of an ounce of calamus aromaticus, and the same quantity of elder flowers, cloves and dried rose leaves, coriander seeds, lavender and bay leaves of each a dram with three drams of storax. Reduce the whole to fine powder which knead into a paste with the soap adding a few grains of musk or ambergris.

When you make this paste into washballs soften it with a little oil of almonds to render this composition more lenient.

*Too much cannot be said in favour of this
washball with regard to its cleaning
and cosmetic property.*

A SCENTED JAR WHICH REMAINS
STRONG FOR MANY YEARS

*R*equired are sweet scented rose petals, lavender flowers, petals of any other sweet scented flowers and a few bay leaves.

Also, half pound bay salt (not bruised) half pound of saltpetre finely bruised with a little common salt. Sixpennyworth of storax, the same of musk and two ounces of cloves. Gather the roses after the dew has dried but before the sun is at its hottest, pick off the petals and rub all flowers put into the jar with common salt. Stir all ingredients well together and keep closely covered for a month. Stir every day. After a month, stir occasionally.

A POMANDER

*T*ake storax an ounce, cloves two drams, benjamin half an ounce, ambergris half a dram, musk fifteen grains, powder of violets a little, incorporate all together with rose water.

TO RENEW THE SCENT OF A POMANDER

*T*ake one grain of civet, and two of musk, or if you double the proportion, it will be much the sweeter; grind them upon a stone with a little rose water; and after wetting your hands with rose water you may work the same in your pomander.

HOW TO DRY ROSES OR OTHER SINGLE FLOWERS WITHOUT WRINKLING

If you would perform the same well in rose leaves, you must in rose time make a choice of such roses as are neither in the bud, nor full blown (for these have the smoothest leaves of all other).

Then take sand, wash it in some change of waters, dry it thoroughly well, either in an oven, or in the sun; and having shallow square or long boxes of four, five or six inches deep, make first an even lay of sand in the bottom upon which lay your rose leaves, one by one (so as none of them touch the other) till you have covered all the sand, then strew sand upon those leaves till your have thinly covered them all, and then make another lay of leaves as before, and so lay upon lay, &c.

Set this box in some warm place in a hot sunny day (and commonly in two hot sunny days they will be thoroughly dry) then take them out carefully with your hand without breaking.

Keep these leaves in glass jars, bound about with paper near a chimney, or stove, for fear of relenting. The red rose leaf is best to be kept in this manner; also take away the stalks of pansies, stock gillyflowers or other single flowers; prick them one by one in sand, pressing down their leaves smooth with more sand laid evenly upon them. And thus you may have rose leaves and other flowers to lay about your basins, windows, &c., all the winter long.

Of course, a great deal of the art of scent-making depends upon the proper blending of perfumes, lavender and rose petals may be blended with good success.

TO MAKE ROSE BEADS FOR A ROSARY

*Gather the roses on a dry day and chop the petals very finely. Put them in a saucepan and barely cover with water. Heat for about an hour, but do not let the mixture boil. Repeat this process for three days and if necessary add more water. The deep black beads made from rose petals are made this rich colour by warming in a rusty pan. It is important never to let the mixture boil, but each day to warm it to a moderate heat. Make the beads by working the pulp with the fingers into balls. When thoroughly well worked and fairly dry, press on to a bodkin to make the holes in the centres of the beads. Until they are perfectly dry, the beads have to be moved frequently on the bodkin or they will be difficult to remove without breaking them.

Held for a few moments in a warm hand these beads give out a pleasing fragrance.

TO PERFUME THE HOUSE WITH SWEET ROSES

Take twelve spoonfuls of very red rose water, the weight of six pence in fine powder of sugar, and boil it on hot embers and coals softly and the house will smell as though it were full of roses, but you must burn the sweet cypress wood before.

A PERFUME FOR CHAMBERS

Take a glassful of rose water, cloves well beaten to powder, a penny weight: then take the fire pan and make it red hot in the fire, and put thereon of the said rose water with the said powder of cloves making it so consume, by little and little but the rose water must be musk, and you shall make a perfume of excellent good odour.

TO MAKE PERFUMES TO BURN

Take half a pound of damask rose buds (the whites cut off), benjamin three ounces beaten to powder, half a quarter of an ounce of musk and as much of ambergris, the like of civet. Beat all these together in a stone mortar, then put in an ounce of sugar, and make it up in cakes and dry them by the fire.

TO MAKE EXCELLENT PERFUMES

Take three ounces of benjamin, lay it all night in damask rose buds cut clean from the whites, beat them very fine in a stone mortar till it comes to a paste, then take it out and mix it with a dram of musk finely beaten, as much civet, mould them up with a little fine sugar and dry them very well and keep them to burn; one at a time is sufficient.

ROSE PASTILS TO BURN

Take benjamin three ounces, storax two ounces, damask rose buds one ounce; grind the roses by themselves and then add the rest also. Then take lignum aloes, amber, fine sugar, civet, powder of cypress, one eighth of a pound; grind these well together. Then mix with gum tragacanth dissolved in rose water and make up into pastils.

EXTRACTING THE ESSENTIAL OILS

Take two pounds of rose leaves, place on a napkin tied round the edges of a basin filled with hot water, and put a dish of cold water upon the leaves, keep the bottom water hot, and change the water at top as soon as it begins to grow warm. By this kind of distillation you will extract a great quantity of the essential oil of the roses, by a process which will not be expensive, and will prove very beneficial.

A SWEET WATER

*T*ake a gallon of spring water, three hand-fuls of roses, a handful of lavender flowers, as much sweet marjoram, the peeling of six oranges, twelve cloves, bruise all these and put to them one ounce of orris powder and four ounces of benjamin.

Put all these into a rose still and draw off the first quart by itself and then a pint, you may draw after that another water from the lees which serve for present use but not keep; put into your quart bottle twelve pennyworth of musk, and in the pint bottle six pennyworth tied in bags and a little juniper sliced very thin as much as will lay on half a crown, two or three spoonfuls will sweeten a basin of water: keep it stopped very close: it will keep a year or two.

Distilled water at first will have very little fragrance, but after being exposed to the heat of the sun about eight days, in a bottle lightly stopped with a bit of paper, it acquires an admirable scent.

AN EXCELLENT WATER FOR THE HEAD AND FOR THE MEMORY

When roses are blown, take a quart of good aquavitae in a glass with a narrow neck and when the roses are half blown take a handful of the leaves without yet seed, put them into the glass and when the marjoram bloweth, take them a handful of their buds, chop them small and put them into the glass. Take also cloves, nutmegs, cinnamon, mace, cardamum, of these an ounce and a half; bruise all these grossly and put it in the glass and when the lavender and rosemary are blown add a handful of these flowers also, shake them well together and stop it close; let it stand ten days in a hot sun: it must be used by anointing the temples and nostrils.

It is said that this water
'fortifies and corroborates the head and memory'.

TO MAKE A RARE SWEET WATER

Take sweet marjoram, damask roses, lavender, rosemary, maudlin, balm, thyme, walnut leaves, pinks, of all a like quantity enough to fill your still, then take of the best orris powder, damask rose powder and storax, of each two ounces; strew one handful or two of your powders upon the herbs, then distill them with a soft fire; tie a little musk in a piece of lawn and hang it in the glass wherein it drops, and when it is all drawn out, take your sweet cakes and mix them with the powders which are left, and lay them among your clothes or with sweet oils, and burn them for perfume.

TO MAKE A SPECIAL SWEET WATER TO PERFUME CLOTHES AFTER BEING WASHED

*T*ake a quart of damask rose water and put it into a glass, put unto it a handful of lavender flowers, two ounces of orris, a dram of musk, the weight of four pence of ambergris, as much civet, four drops of oil of cloves, stop this close, and set it in the sun a fortnight, put one spoonful of this water into a basin of common water and put it into a glass and so sprinkle your clothes therewith in your folding.

The dregs left in the bottom (when the water is spent) will make as much more, if you keep them, and put fresh rose water to it.

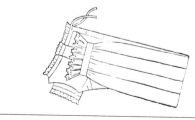

SWEET WATER OF THE BEST KIND
USING A THOUSAND ROSES

Take a thousand damask roses, two good handfuls of lavender tops, a three-penny weight of mace, two ounces of cloves bruised, a quart of running water; put a little water into the bottom of an earthen pot and then put in your roses and lavender, with the spices little by little, and in the putting in, always knead them down with your fist, and so continue it until you have wrought up all your roses and lavender and in the working put in always a little of your water: then put in your pot close and let it stand in four days, in which time every morning and evening put in your hand and pull from the bottom of your pot the said roses, working it for a time, and then distill it, and having in the glass of water a grain or two of musk wrapped up in a piece of sarcenet or fine cloth.

TO PERFUME GLOVES

*T*ake rose water and angelica water, and put to them the powder of cloves, ambergris, musk and lignum aloes, benjamin and calamus aromaticus; boil them, hang them in the sun to dry and turn them often, and thus three times wet them and dry them again. Otherwise take rose water and wet your gloves therein, then hang them up till they be almost dry; then take half an ounce of benjamin, and grind it with the oil of almonds, and rub it on the gloves till it be almost dried in: then take twenty grains of musk, and grind them together with oil of almonds and so rub it on the gloves and then hang them up to dry, or let them dry in your bosom, and so after use them at your pleasure.

A VERY RARE AND PLEASANT
DAMASK WATER

*T*ake a quart of malmsey lees, or a quart of malmsey simply, damask rose leaves four handfuls, and as many of red, one handful of marjoram, of basil as much, of lavender four handfuls, bay leaves one good handful, the peels of six oranges, or; one handful of the tender leaves of walnut, of benjamin half an ounce, of calamus aromaticus as much, of camphor four drams, of cloves one ounce, then take a pottle of running water and put in all these spices bruised in to your water and malmsey together in a close stopped pot with a good handful of rosemary, and let them stand for the space of six days, then distill it with a soft fire: then set it in the sun sixteen days with four grains of musk bruised. This quantity will make three quarts of water.

*As a gift, nothing could be better than a bottle of
sweet perfume made by the giver. The cost will be
trifling, though the pains bestowed may not be,
and if a dainty cut-glass bottle be procured, the
whole tied with a piece of white satin ribbon,
bearing the name of the recipient, and an
appropriate greeting, the result will be most
successful. Should the sender be cunning with the
brush, a spray of the flower represented by the
scent might be painted upon the ribbon!*

TO MAKE SWEET WATER

*T*ake damask roses at discretion, basil, sweet marjoram, lavender, walnut leaves, of each two handfuls, rosemary one handful, a little balm, cloves cinnamon, bay leaves, lemon and orange pills of each a few; pour upon these as much white wine as will conveniently wet them and let them infuse ten or twelve days: then distill it off.

Dry roses put to the nose to smell do comfort the brain and the heart and quencheth spirits.

TO MAKE THE BEST SWEET WATER

Take three pints of rose water, half a pint of orange flower water, musk, ambergris, lignum aloes, twenty five grains, civet fifteen grains, benjamin four ounces, storax one ounce, all in fine powder; mix all these well together, and put them in a brass pot, covering it very close with linen, and set it to boil in a kettle full of water the space of three hours; then pour off the clear, and put upon the remaining matter the same quantity of fresh rose and orange flower water, and five or six grains of civet, then of the rest you make pastils.

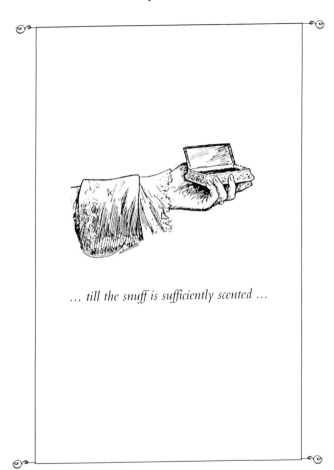

... till the snuff is sufficiently scented ...

METHOD OF SCENTING SNUFF

The flowers that most readily communicate their flavour to snuff are orange flowers, muck roses, jasmine and tuberoses.

You must procure a box lined with dry white paper; in this strew your snuff on the bottom about the thickness of an inch, over which place a thin layer of flowers, then another layer of snuff, and continue to lay your flowers and snuff alternately in this matter, until the box is full.

After they have lain together four and twenty hours, sift your snuff through a sieve to separate it from the flowers, which are to be thrown away, and fresh ones applied in their room in the former method.

Continue to do this till the snuff is sufficiently scented; then put it into a canister. Keep the canister close stopped.

THE ROSE LEAF CUSHION

'Gather ye rosebuds while ye may,
Old Time is still a-flying'

*T*hus through the ages have the poets sung of the sweetness and beauty of the rose. The word has almost become symbolical of golden summer and sunny skies.

Collecting the rose petals -
The hobby of collecting rose petals as they fall is a fascinating one during the summer months - all the more delightful when a practical use can be found for their sweetness, although they no longer blossom the garden.

A brilliant and warm day is the one on which to
cull rose petals for future use.

Drying the rose petals -

After they have been collected in a basket, each petal should be separated, and put to dry in the sunshine. Choose a room which is little used for this purpose. Some large lids from cardboard boxes may be placed on the table.

As the full-blown roses and petals are collected on every succeeding fine day, they should be placed on the lids of the boxes and dried.

A muslin bag -

Before this process is completed, a square bag of muslin, large enough to form a good-sized cushion, should be made, and as the petals dry, they can be dropped into it without further handling.

When the bag appears full, the rose leaves should be thoroughly shaken up, and more leaves added if necessary, as it must be well filled to make a soft and attractive cushion.

A rose coloured covering -

Such a cushion requires a dainty covering. Perhaps a soft, rose-coloured satin would be the most suitable, a yard and a quarter of satin making a good square. This must be folded in half, and then one half rolled up to keep it clean, whilst the other half is pinned on to a drawing board.

An appropriate motto or verse -

Sketch or trace some roses on to the satin. It may also please the artist to sketch in a favourite motto or verse, such as,

- in quaintly shaped letters, to add a pretty, decorative finish.

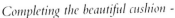

Completing the beautiful cushion -

Each side of the square of satin is now ready to be sewn up and converted into a beautiful and artistic cushion-cover.

To return to the muslin bag or cushion which contains the rose-petals. Several packets of 'petal-dust' may be emptied into this, which will add a delightfully aromatic perfume.

Another way to accentuate the sweetness of the roses is to add some pot-pourri.

Firmly stitch the muslin bag along the top, so that neither rose-petals nor pot-pourri can escape. Slip the satin cover the muslin bag, and a delightfully dainty cushion is complete.

These cushions are charming, containing the petals of old-world flowers and the distinctive perfume which one instinctively associates with this country.

*Another practical adaptation of the rose leaf
cushion idea. It might take the form of
one of those pretty triangular cushions that are
so eminently restful when fixed on a
high-backed chair so that they support
the nape of the neck of the sitter.*

'... As for the strange connection subsisting between perfume and the mental processes, ... nothing so instantaneously evokes and revives forgotten memories as the sense of some odour in affinity with events or scenes long since gone from the mind. Nor is it always easy to relate the scent in question; I cannot, for example account for the circumstance that the odour of roses invariably recalls to me the parlour of a little seaside cottage in which, when a child, I spent many very happy days. Certainly I have smelt roses since then in hundreds of various gardens and the memories evoked are not mere indefinite recollections. They are vivid, sharp, instinct with life. ... As the magic odour floats over our nervous surfaces, the heart throbs again with emotions and hopes of which we have long ceased to have experience. Time rolls back, the atmosphere around us is changed - we are young again!'

Written in 1896 in Midsummer.

Bibliography:

These recipes for roses have been compiled from many different sources and although many of these ancient 'receipts' ask for rose leaves, we must assume that rose petals were the true ingredient. Books, magazines and ephemera consulted include::

Book of Simples 17th century
Choice & Experimented Receipts 1668
Country Contentments 1653
Delights for Ladies 1594
Englishwoman's Domestic Magazine 19th century
Every Woman's Encyclopaedia 19th century
The Art of Cookery 1784
The Toilet of Flora 1772
The English Housewife 1625
The Queen's Closet 1662

THE ETIQUETTE COLLECTION
Collect the set!

ETIQUETTE FOR COFFEE LOVERS
Fresh coffee - the best welcome in the world!
Enjoy the story of coffee drinking, etiquette and recipes.

ETIQUETTE FOR CHOCOLATE LOVERS
Temptation through the years.
A special treat for all chocolate lovers.

THE ETIQUETTE OF NAMING THE BABY
'A good name keeps its lustre in the dark.'
Old English Proverb

THE ETIQUETTE OF AN ENGLISH TEA
How to serve a perfect English afternoon tea;
traditions, recipes and how to read your fortune in the
tea-leaves afterwards.

THE ETIQUETTE OF ENGLISH PUDDINGS
Traditional recipes for good old-fashioned
puddings - together with etiquette notes for serving.

ETIQUETTE FOR GENTLEMEN
*'If you have occasion to use your handkerchief
do so as noiselessly as possible.'*

Copper Beech Gift Books
are designed and printed
in Great Britain.